EDISON EXPERIMENTS

YOU CAN DO

EDISON

Text by Marjorie Van de Water of Science Service

Photographs by Fremont Davis

EXPERIMENTS YOU CAN DO

Based on the Original Notebooks of

THOMAS ALVA EDISON

PREPARED UNDER THE DIRECTION OF
INTERNATIONAL EDISON BIRTHDAY
CELEBRATION COMMITTEE OF THE
THOMAS ALVA EDISON FOUNDATION

Harper & Brothers, Publishers, New York

EDISON EXPERIMENTS YOU CAN DO

ACKNOWLEDGEMENTS

The famous laboratory notebooks of Thomas Alva Edison are housed at the Edison National Monument, West Orange, New Jersey.
The editors wish to thank Fremont Davis of Science Service, Washington, D. C., for his assistance in setting up the experiments.

CONTENTS

INTRODUCTION
by Charles Edison

Fear of failure, Charles F. Kettering once told me, is one of the hobgoblins that haunt young men and women interested in the sciences. Until we understand, he said, that we can learn as much from our failures as we can from our successes, this pesky hobgoblin will continue practicing its witchcraft.

The late "Boss Ket" was not afraid of failure; neither was Thomas Edison.

This book will introduce you to some experiments for which a definite result is promised. Most experiments are not so. Experimentation in its truest sense is launching forth into uncharted seas. Conceivably, you may know where you would like to arrive, but you probably won't know which path to follow.

I commend you to conducting in the best possible

manner the experiments set forth in this fine book. I recommend, also, that you not feel downhearted if things don't work out exactly as you think they should. Remember that "Boss Ket" and Thomas Edison weren't always right the first time, either.

One of the most positive memories I have of my father demonstrates, to a marked degree, one of the qualities needed by a good experimenter. That quality is Interest—with a capital I.

In 1914, a disastrous fire ruined his expansive factories in West Orange, New Jersey. At the height of the conflagration, with much of his personal fortune going up in flames before his very eyes, he called me to his side and said:

"Where's your mother? Get her over here, and her friends too. They'll never see a fire like this again."

Disaster that would have crumbled many men was all around him. Yet, Thomas Edison's capital-I Interest in everything around him still urged him to want others to experience a truly spectacular event.

On another occasion, when Father was knee-deep in trying to unlock the secrets of a better battery, one of his assistants grew increasingly dejected. Failure after failure had piled up, one upon the other.

The assistant approached Mr. Edison one day and, despairingly, suggested that Mr. Edison must be ready to quit after making 50,000 different tests without success.

"You must be pretty downhearted with the lack of progress," the assistant said.

"Downhearted?" replied Mr. Edison. "Why should I feel downhearted? We've made a lot of progress. At least we know 50,000 things that won't work!"

I remember the long, happy hours my father spent in his laboratory. To him, work was not work, if you were interested in what you were doing.

In the end, his persistence won out; and after more than 50,000 experiments he produced a revolutionary new nickel-iron-alkaline battery. That was more than fifty years ago and the nickel-iron-alkaline cells are still going strong today.

Every event in your life can't be spectacular, but almost everything you do can be of great interest if you will let it be so.

Again, I hope you will find this book of *Edison Experiments You Can Do* a stimulating experience.

EDISON EXPERIMENTS

YOU CAN DO

You (Edison) have been equally successful as a pioneer, executive and organizer. Your construction of the electric lamp has to a great extent made the development of a great electrical industry possible. The great technical creators, of which you are one of the most successful, have produced in the course of a century an entirely new situation to which mankind has not yet adapted himself—

Albert Einstein

THOMAS ALVA EDISON

Many persons think that ideas for revolutionary inventions pop into the inventor's mind fully developed in a "flash of genius."

This is not the way Edison produced his inventions. The electric light, the phonograph, and the microphone were the result of long hours of tireless work, patient experimenting, hard thinking, and a refusal to be discouraged. Edison was fond of saying, "Genius is one per cent inspiration and 99 per cent perspiration," and "Genius is hard work, stick-to-it-iveness and common sense."

Another characteristic of Edison was his patient, systematic way of working. When he was a young boy and first used a public library, he started at one corner of a shelf and read all the books on it, one after the other, resolving not to stop until he knew the contents of the whole library.

When he experimented on a problem, Edison would not give up until he had found the solution. He never became discouraged, and he could work the clock around without showing exhaustion.

One of his associates for many years, W. S. Mallory, said, "I shouldn't wonder if his experiments on the [alkaline storage] battery ran up pretty near to fifty-thousand."

Mallory has described a typical work day when Edison was experimenting on the battery:

"About 7 or 7:30 A.M. he would go down to the laboratory and experiment, only stopping for a short time at noon to eat a lunch sent down from the house. About 6 o'clock the carriage would call to take him to dinner, from which he would return by 7:30 or 8 o'clock to resume work. The carriage came again at midnight to take him home, but frequently had to wait until 2 or 3 o'clock, and sometimes return without him, as he had decided to continue all night."

This schedule went on for more than five months, seven days a week.

We often expect boys who always make good grades in school to turn out to be geniuses. Edison was an exception. Because of illness and the family's various moves, he did not start school until he was eight years old. After he had attended for only three months, he is reported to have heard the schoolmaster say that he was "addled," and in a storm of anger young Edison ran home. His mother, too, was furious. Next morning, she visited the school with her Alva, as he was called in childhood, and saw the schoolmaster. There was an angry scene and the mother withdrew her son from the school to teach him herself. She felt qualified to do this because she had taught school before her marriage.

Young Edison had been bored with lessons when he was forced to learn them at school, but his mother allowed the boy to study and read what attracted his interest, and she found him an enthusiastic and industrious student. Science and nature always fascinated him.

At the age of ten or eleven he started to do chemical experiments. With every penny of spending money he bought chemicals from the drug store until most of the cellar was filled with bottles. He tested each chemical until he had satisfied his curiosity about what it would do.

Although Edison gained his world-wide fame almost entirely in the field of electricity, he always thought of himself as a chemist.

Thomas Alva Edison was born at Milan, Ohio, on

February 11, 1847. He came into a world that was becoming excited about the interesting new possibilities of electricity.

Thomas Alva Edison was born in this brick house in Milan, Ohio, on February 11, 1847. The house is now a museum. (*Thomas Alva Edison Foundation*)

Seven years earlier, in 1840, Samuel Morse had received a patent on his electromagnetic telegraph. In 1844, the world was thrilled when Morse tapped out the message "What hath God wrought" in the first long-distance telegraph transmission from his office at 7th and E streets in Washington, D. C., to Baltimore, Maryland.

Now through electricity, instantaneous communication over many miles was a reality.

When Edison was about ten years old, he and a young friend set up a telegraph line between their houses. They used sections of common stovepipe wire, and made insulators by slipping bottles over nails they had driven into convenient posts or trees. Their telegraph keys were pieces of spring brass. The other boy could not receive the code very well and would sometimes go outside and yell over to ask Alva what he had said. This angered Edison, who evidently felt that it showed distrust of the new invention.

Edison's interest in chemistry was so great that his limited pocket money was not enough to keep him supplied with chemicals for his experiments. He heard of a job opening selling newspapers on the train to Detroit. In addition to spending money, the job would also provide him with leisure in Detroit. During the long layover in the city, he could go to the big stores to buy equipment and chemicals that were unavailable in his home town, and he could also browse in the Detroit Public Library.

He obtained his parents' consent, and applied for and got the job. There was extra room in the baggage and mail car, and Alva was permitted to set up his laboratory on the train. He worked hard at his experiments when he was not going through the cars peddling papers, fruit, and candy.

Edison was about ten years old when this picture was taken.
(*Science Service*)

When Alva got home after his long day on the train, there was little time to practice on the telegraph before he had to go to bed. But he put his ingenuity to work and secured unlimited practice.

His father enjoyed reading the newspapers, and Alva always brought home a bundle of "returnables," papers left over from the day's sales. His father would sit up and read them, while Alva was hustled off to bed. One night Edison had an idea. He gave his friend the extra papers, and told his father that he would ask the boy to send the news to him over their telegraph. This was done, and Alva had practice not only in reading code, but in taking down the messages in longhand for his father to read.

His chemical experiments received a severe setback about this time. The train was passing over a rough stretch of track when a sudden lurch jarred a stick of phosphorus off the shelf and it burst into flames on the floor. The whole car was soon ablaze. A conductor rushed in, put out the fire and saved the car. The conductor was so angry with the young experimenter that at the next station he threw the boy and all his chemicals off the train.

Edison was still a boy when he became deaf. Many stories are told about how this occurred. One version is that the angry conductor who tossed Edison off the train damaged the boy's hearing with a furious blow on the side of the head.

Another version says that it happened when a conductor was trying to help the boy climb onto the train. He pulled Edison up by the ears. Edison felt something snap in his head and from that time on the deafness progressed.

A family doctor is reported to have said that deafness was hereditary in the Edison family, and that Edison would have become deaf no matter what happened to him.

However it may have originated, deafness stimulated Edison's interest in sound devices—the microphone, the telephone, and the phonograph. Edison always considered his deafness a great advantage, not a handicap.

In a telegraph office, he said, he could hear only the instrument on the table at which he sat and, unlike the other operators, he was not bothered by the clattering of other instruments. On the busiest streets he was not annoyed by traffic noises. At work he was not distracted by trivial conversations going on near him. Edison could always concentrate on the problem on which he was working.

While Edison was working on the train, an incident occurred that had an important effect on his later life. The train was stopped at Mount Clemens station while some of the cars were being switched. As Alva was standing on the platform he saw the small son of the station agent playing with the gravel on the track. Suddenly one of the cars came rolling down the track without locomotive or train crew. It was headed for the child. Alva dropped his newspapers, grabbed the child, and jumped out of the way. He and the child were safe, but by a very small margin.

The boy's father was so grateful to young Edison that he offered to train him to be a telegraph operator. This was Edison's introduction to serious telegraphy.

When he went to Mount Clemens to learn telegraphy, Edison already knew how to send and receive code. He also brought with him the set of telegraph instruments he had made himself at a gunsmith's shop in Detroit.

With his usual enthusiasm, Edison devoted at least eighteen hours a day to learning the new job, and he kept this up for three or four months. Then he worked for a short time as a telegraph operator in Port Huron, Michigan. These long hours of practice may have been the start of his unusual habits of work and sleep. When he became interested in a problem, he would work right through the night. He seemed to need very little sleep. But perhaps he got more than he or his associates realized, because he used to lie down on a sofa at intervals and catch a few minutes of sleep. When he awoke, he was instantly alert and ready to plunge into work again. It was as if he had never been away from his desk or work-bench.

He was sixteen when he got his first regular job as a railway operator at Stratford Junction in Canada. His pay was $25 per month. He liked to work the night shift.

He would spend the whole day in reading and experimenting. Sometimes it was difficult for him to stay awake during the long hours of the night, especially when work was slack. He got into the habit of sleeping in a chair for a few minutes at a time. But he taught the night yardman his signal, and if the station was called, the watchman would awaken him.

It was the custom, however, to require the operator to send the signal "6" (*dah*-di-di-di-dit) every hour to show that he was awake and on the job. This regulation was the inspiration for one of Edison's first inventions. He made notches in the rim of a small wheel. At night he connected the wheel in the telegraph circuit in such a way that as it revolved each hour it would automatically send the signal for the "6."

When he became a telegrapher, Edison joined an unusual company of young men. They were well paid—as wages in those days went—and they were greatly in demand because the traffic was always beyond the capacity of the men available to send the telegrams.

Edison, though still in his teens, was unusually capable. He could send messages rapidly and accurately, and could take the messages he received as fast as they were transmitted. And his handwriting was legible. Many of the operators in those days were erratic and irresponsible. They were drifters, who would go without warning from place to place, encouraged by the knowledge that they could always get a good job wherever they happened to be.

But others became famous in transportation, journalism, and public affairs. They included Theodore N. Vail, later president of the Bell Telephone System; Andrew Carnegie, the financier and philanthropist; Frank A. Munsey, magazine and newspaper publisher; A. B. Chandler, president of the Postal Telegraph and Cable Company, and Guy Carleton, a successful dramatist.

The difficulties that Edison had in keeping jobs were due to his love for science and experimenting. Once he was fired for carrying out orders he had received. Edison told this story of the incident:

"About 9 o'clock the superintendent handed me a dispatch which he said was very important, and which I must get off at once. The wire at the time was very busy and I asked if I should break in. I got

Edison at work in his chemistry laboratory—the great inventor always thought of himself as a chemist. (*Thomas Alva Edison Foundation*)

orders to do so, and acting under those orders of the superintendent, I broke in and tried to send the dispatch; but the other operator would not permit it, and the struggle continued for ten minutes. Finally I got possession of the wire and sent the message. The superintendent of telegraph, who then lived in Adrian and went to his office in Toledo every day, happened that day to be in the Western Union office uptown—and it was the superintendent I was really struggling with! In about twenty minutes he arrived livid with rage and I was discharged on the spot. I informed him that the general superintendent had told me to break in and send the dispatch, but the general superintendent then and there repudiated the whole thing. Their families were socially close, so I was sacrificed. My faith in human nature got a slight jar."

Although he was a good operator, especially at taking messages, Edison was constantly trying to improve himself and learn more. He taught himself to be a rapid reader so that he could sense the meaning of a whole line at a single glance.

This skill was a great help to him because of the tremendous quantities of books, scientific journals, magazines and newspapers he read. Because he made a specialty of receiving the press messages for the newspapers, the newspaper men would allow him to go to the newspaper office after the paper went to press at 3 A.M. and take home all the "exchanges" he wanted. He would then lay them across the foot of his bed. He never slept more than four or five hours, and when he awoke he would read the papers until it was time to get up for dinner.

"I thus kept posted," Edison said, "and knew from their activity every member of Congress, and what committees they were on; and all about the topical doings, as well as the prices of breadstuffs in all the primary markets. I was in a much better position than most operators to call on my imagination to supply missing words or sentences which were frequent in those days of old, rotten wires, badly insulated—especially on stormy nights. Upon such occasions I had to supply in some cases one-fifth of the whole matter—pure guessing—but I got caught only once.

"There had been some kind of convention in Virginia, in which John Minor Botts was the leading figure. There was great excitement about it and two votes had been taken in the convention on the two days. There was no doubt that the vote the next day would go a certain way. A very bad storm came up about 10 o'clock, and my wire worked very badly. Then there was a cessation of all signals; then I made out the words 'Minor Botts.' The next was a New York item. I filled in a paragraph about the convention and how the vote had gone, as I was sure it would. But next day I learned that instead of there being a vote the convention had adjourned without action until the day after."

During the first five years he worked as a teleggrapher, Edison traveled all over the Midwest in search of a better job, or at least a different job. Then he decided to go East, where he got a job in Boston with Western Union. In Boston Edison first became acquainted with Michael Faraday's works. One night he was lucky enough to find a complete set of Faraday's writings. He took them home at 4 A.M. and read steadily until breakfast time. Later he said:

"I think I must have tried about everything in those books. His explanations were simple. He used no mathematics. He was the master experimenter. I don't think there were many copies of Faraday's works sold in those days. The only people who did anything in electricity were the telegraphers and the opticians making simple school apparatus to demonstrate the principles."

Faraday's famous "Diary" may have been the inspiration for Edison's system of keeping notebooks. During the earliest years Edison jotted his notes down on loose sheets of paper which he then tied up in bundles or pasted into large scrapbooks. In 1876, when he moved to Menlo Park, New Jersey, and at last had a real laboratory, Edison adopted a new system for his laboratory notebooks. He used a standard-size book, about eight and a half by six inches and containing about 200 pages. In sixty years Edison filled 3,400 of these notebooks. It took

150 notebooks to record the experiments he made in developing his battery. The whole collection is now carefully stored in an underground vault in the Edison National Monument in West Orange, New Jersey. For Edison, too, was a "master experimenter."

"The only way to keep ahead of the procession is to experiment," Edison himself once said. "If you don't, the other fellow will. When there's no experimenting, there's no progress. Stop experimenting and you go backward. If anything goes wrong, experiment until you get to the very bottom of the trouble."

It was in Boston that Edison applied for his first patent—on the electrical vote recorder. This was a device that made it possible for a legislator to press one of two buttons on his desk, and instantaneously his vote, "aye" or "nay," would be recorded and counted electrically. The invention was taken to Washington and exhibited at the Capitol. But the chairman, after watching it work, crushed Edison's hopes.

"Young man," he said, "if there is any invention on earth that we don't want down here, it is this." It would spoil the system of filibustering, he explained. When the legislature wants to delay action, a great deal of time is occupied in calling the members' names and recording and adding their votes.

This, the chairman declared, is one of the greatest weapons in the hands of a minority to prevent bad legislation.

Edison, greatly distressed, resolved never again to develop an invention until he was sure that there would be a demand for it.

His next important invention was a stock ticker which brought to stock brokers, businessmen, newspapers and others, the results of the trading at the Stock Exchange. Edison took this invention to New York. When he left Boston he had just enough money for the trip, and arrived in New York without a cent. It was early in the morning, and Edison was hungry, so his first thought was of a hearty breakfast. He had planned to look up a friend and borrow enough money to tide him over until he found a job. He learned that his friend had moved, and when at last he located him, it was only to find that he too was without work. The best the friend could do was to lend Edison a dollar.

Edison gave considerable thought to what he should have for breakfast that morning. He decided on apple dumplings and coffee, and later said that he had never had a better tasting breakfast.

Not long afterward, Edison was asked by General Marshall Lefferts, of the Gold and Stock Telegraph Company, to try to improve his stock ticker. After

Edison had been working on the problem for some time, and had developed a number of improvements and obtained many patents, General Lefferts asked the inventor how much he wanted for his work. Edison believed that he was entitled to $5,000, but he was willing to settle for $3,000. Still he hesitated to name such a large figure and asked the General to make an offer.

"How would $40,000 strike you?" asked the General.

Edison nearly fainted. A few days later he signed a contract without reading it and received the first check he ever had—a check for $40,000! He did not even know how one went about cashing a check, or what he was going to do with all that money.

In 1876, when he was not quite thirty years old, Edison moved to Menlo Park. There, at last, he had a laboratory, especially planned and equipped for his experiments. And there he directed a staff of assistants, who worked on his inventions. The concept of organized research was one of his most important inventions. Some years later, Edison moved his laboratory to West Orange, New Jersey, where he established an industrial research laboratory where a group of men worked together to produce new products. It was the first of the more than four thousand such laboratories in the United States today.

At Menlo Park were developed the carbon telephone transmitter, the phonograph, and the incandescent lamp. (You will read more about these inven-

Edison's early phonograph records resembled dictating
machine cylinders. Edison is shown examining an early record.
(*Edison National Monument*)

tions, and about Edison's methods of working, in the Experiments chapters of this book.) Here Edison worked on the dynamo, the electric railway, the megaphone, the tasimeter—a sensitive instrument for the measurement of temperature—and continued his earlier work on the quadruplex, the sextuplex, the multiplex, and the automatic telegraph.

One of the most interesting events in the life of Edison concerns his search for the best material for use in the filament of the incandescent lamp. Edison found that a certain species of bamboo grown in Japan was suitable for filaments in the lamps. But he was constantly on the lookout for something better, or for a larger supply of something as good. Edison learned that John C. Branner of Brooklyn had an expert knowledge of the kinds of plants he desired. Mr. Branner had studied various species of palms that grow in Brazil, and he knew that the fibers of one of the palms might be just what Edison wanted. But they did not prove to be superior to the Japanese specimens.

Later Edison sent an expedition to explore the wilds of Cuba and Jamaica. He sent two other men to South America where they experienced tremendous hardship, disease, and the attacks of hostile Indians, wild animals, and poisonous snakes. One of the men, as Edison said, found what he wanted but then lost the place where he found it, so he might as well have never found it at all.

The final scout sent out by Edison in the search for filament fibers was a young schoolteacher who

The dynamo room of the first Edison Electric Lighting Station in New York City—the station began operation in 1882. (*Edison National Monument*)

went to the Far East to find a better bamboo than the one Edison had been using. His trip was very successful but by the time he returned on February 22, 1889, exactly a year from the hour he set out, Edison had discovered how to make a carbon filament by carbonizing cellulose which had been squirted out through a die forming a fine thread.

When Edison was working on the incandescent light bulb, a dramatic and painful incident occurred which showed how little was known at the time about the great brightness that could be obtained from such a light. Here is an entry from Edison's notebook dated January 28, 1879.

"Owing to the enormous power of the light [alloy of nickel] my eye commenced to pain after 7 hours work and I had to quit.

"Suffered the pains of hell with my eye last night from 10 P.M. to 4 A.M. when I got to sleep with a big dose of morphine. Eyes better, do not pain much at 4 P.M. but I doze today."

Anxiety must have been added to the physical pain when Edison thought of the possibility of permanent damage to his eyesight.

With the passing of the years, Edison never ceased to do creative work and he never stopped working amazingly long hours. During World War I, when he was in his seventies, he put his inventiveness to work to help the United States win the war. One of his inventions was a sound device to detect the presence of submarines and torpedoes. He served as chairman of the Naval Consulting Board and worked on a series of problems for the Navy, and gave his services to the Government without charge.

In addition to developing needed weapons of defense, Edison set about filling critical shortages of important chemicals such as carbolic acid, needed for explosives, which he manufactured synthetically. The latter part of Edison's life was devoted to the study of plants grown in the United States from which rubber could be extracted. Within three years,

This is one of the best known portraits of the inventor of the electric light. (*Science Service*)

he tested more than 17,000 plants and developed his own method of extracting rubber.

In 1887, Edison built the laboratory at West Orange that is now the Edison Laboratory National Monument. During the forty-four years of his life which he spent at West Orange he was granted 520 patents covering such things as electric motors and generators, incandescent and fluorescent lamps, continuous nickel and copper plating, an electric locomotive, the depositing metals in a vacuum, magnetic concentration and briquetting of iron ore, the motion-picture camera, and scores of improvements in the recording and reproduction of sound.

On October 20, 1928, the forty-ninth anniversary of the invention of the incandescent lamp, Edison received the Congressional Medal for his services to science and the arts. And in the following year, there was a world-wide celebration of the half-century of the electric light. The United States Post Office issued a special stamp in honor of the occasion.

Edison never lost interest in the world about him. New inventions and discoveries excited him as much when he was in his eighties as they had when he was in his teens. At the time Edison died, in 1931, at the age of eighty-four, the United States was suffering from the Great Depression. But Edison refused to be discouraged. In one of his last public statements he restated his faith:

"My message to you is: Be courageous. I have lived a long time. I have seen history repeat itself again and again. I have seen many depressions in business. Always America has come out stronger and more prosperous. Be as brave as your fathers before you. Have faith. Go forward."

EDISON EXPERIMENTS

CARBON BUTTON

Many of Edison's discoveries were not inventions in the sense of being mechanisms or devices that could be put to immediate practical use.

Some of his most important discoveries were observations of unusual or previously unknown properties of nature. When he recorded in his notebooks an experiment that brought to light such properties, he called his discovery a "phenomenon."

One such phenomenon was the behavior of carbon in the form of lamp black or powdered graphite (then called plumbago). Edison's famous "carbon button" was made from lamp black which he carefully gathered from the chimneys of a large number of smoking kerosene lamps. Earlier Edison had found that such finely divided carbon could be used to vary the strength of current flowing through a wire. He learned this in the year 1873, when he was trying to find a way to speed up the transmission of telegraph messages over a long under-ocean cable.

When current flows in a wire, the movement is of small particles called electrons. The electrons go in at one end of the wire. As they move through the wire one electron pushes another, and that one in turn pushes still another until the same number of electrons as entered the wire go to the ground at the other end.

Anything in the wire that slows the movement of the electrons is called resistance; it is like the resistance met by a sled going downhill when it hits a bare patch of dirt that is not slippery.

The resistance of a small (thin) wire is greater than that of a large (thick) wire. The resistance of a long wire is greater than that of a short wire. The resistance of a transoceanic cable would be tremendous.

In order to conduct his cable experiments, Edison needed to duplicate on a small scale in his laboratory the conditions of the long cable. To produce a resistance to the passage of electric current that could compare to the resistance of a 3,000-mile-long cable, he pressed finely ground graphite into glass tubes and inserted wires in the graphite at the ends of the tubes. By putting many of the tubes end to end, he was able to approximate the resistance of the cable. Edison planned to use the connected graphite-filled tubes in his experiments to test what would happen in the cable under various conditions.

Unfortunately, they did not serve his purpose.

The tubes did give the resistance he needed. But he found that he could not keep the resistance constant. The slightest pressure on the end of the tube, even a vibration in the wires, varied the resistance. When Edison saw that the arrangement would not do, he laid it aside.

He did not forget it, however. He did not regard the experiment as a failure. Four years later he remembered the "phenomenon" of the behavior of carbon and put it to another kind of use.

He was then at work trying to find some way to transmit the vibrations caused in a telephone diaphragm by the human voice. He thought of the curious behavior of the graphite in the glass tubes. He recalled that vibrations of the wire had altered the resistance of the graphite to electric currents.

Edison now experimented with graphite in various forms. He used a stick of graphite adjusted so that it would touch lightly on a spring attached to a telephone diaphragm. When a person spoke into the telephone, the diaphragm would vibrate, causing a change in pressure on the spring and so on the graphite. This, in turn, caused a variation in the current passing through the graphite.

After experimenting with several solid materials including sticks of graphite and finding them unsat-

isfactory, Edison tried tufts of silk floss coated with graphite.

Edison found that he could get a tremendous sensitivity using the different forms of graphite with the telephone. The instrument would pick up the faintest sounds—a whisper, the touch of a finger, the footstep of a fly, even a softly exhaled breath. This was the basis for the invention of the microphone. But the reproduction of speech was not distinct. The instrument would shout or blare but it would not speak clearly.

Edison continued his search for a better material. One day he happened to be distracted from his work by the annoying smoking of his kerosene lamp. Glancing at the lamp, he noticed the intense black of the smoked-up chimney. Edison was curious about this deposit and as soon as the lamp had cooled a little he wiped off some of the black and examined it.

It was not long afterward that Edison gathered the black from many chimneys and pressed it into a mold to make the first carbon button. Soon he set up banks of lamps and put them all to smoking in what he called his carbon factory. He kept assistants busy gathering the lamp black and pressing it into buttons.

These buttons he turned to many uses. The carbon button solved the problem of the telephone trans-

mitter and is used in the mouthpiece of your telephone today.

EXPERIMENT 1. For this experiment you will need a straight glass tube about eight inches long, ⅜ inches in diameter, and open at both ends. You

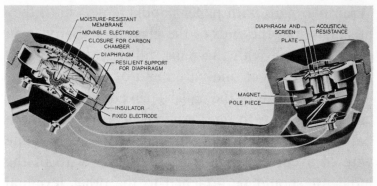

MOISTURE-RESISTANT MEMBRANE
MOVABLE ELECTRODE
CLOSURE FOR CARBON CHAMBER
DIAPHRAGM
RESILIENT SUPPORT FOR DIAPHRAGM
INSULATOR
FIXED ELECTRODE
DIAPHRAGM AND SCREEN
ACOUSTICAL RESISTANCE
PLATE
MAGNET
POLE PIECE

Fig. 1. Cut-away of a modern telephone showing how carbon is still used in the transmitter. (*Bell Telephone Laboratories*)

can get a glass tube for a few cents at most drug stores. If the tube is too long, it is easy to cut it to the right length. Scratch the tube with a file at the length you want. Your scratch need not be deep or go all the way around the tube. Hold the scratched side away from you. Place your thumbs on either side of the scratch, but on the side nearest you, and press evenly with both thumbs against the tube. The tube should snap, making a clean break at the file scratch. It is best to cover the tube with a towel to avoid cuts.

You will also need some powdered graphite. You can buy this in a plastic squeeze-tube applicator. Graphite is sold in hardware stores for use in lubricating such things as door locks.

Bare both ends of two lengths of insulated bell wire. Wrap two nails with paper handkerchiefs until they fit snugly into the ends of the glass tube. Before you close the tube with the nails, fill it with powdered graphite. Connect one bared end of each length of wire to the heads of the nails. Then connect the other end of one wire to one terminal of a 6-volt lantern battery, and the other end of the second wire to one wire of a current indicator. The other wire of the indicator should be attached to the other terminal of the battery.

If you do not have a current indicator, you can make one using a compass such as a Boy Scout's compass. Wrap insulated bell wire or fine, varnish-covered magnet wire around the compass several times so that the wire coil is in line with the needle when it is pointing to north. As electric current passes through the wire, the needle of the compass will move; the larger the current, the greater will be the swing of the needle. When in use, the current indicator should lie as flat as possible so that the needle will not stick, and it should be turned so that the needle points to north when no current is flowing.

EXPERIMENT 2. Press some powdered carbon into a small metal mold until it holds together in the form of a button. For a mold you can use a small metal measure such as a teaspoon kitchen measure, a teaspoon, or the little metal measure that sometimes comes in a can of baby food. Use bell wire to connect the metal measure to one end of the wire coil around the compass. Attach the other end of the coil to the negative terminal of the battery (usually marked with a minus sign). Then attach one end of another piece of wire to the positive terminal of the battery and dip the other end into the carbon in the measure. (See Fig. 2.) The current is now flowing from the battery through the carbon and metal measure, then through your home-made current indicator and back to the battery. Notice the swing of the compass needle, indicating that a current is passing through the circuit. This experiment shows that powdered carbon transmits electricity.

EXPERIMENT 3. Use the same set-up as in Experiment 2. Place a copper penny on the carbon in the measure. With the same wire that you dipped into the carbon in Experiment 2, touch the penny lightly,

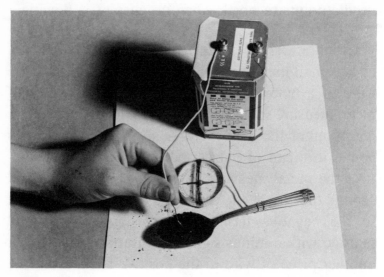

Fig. 2. Current indicator, made by wrapping wire around a compass, shows that current is flowing from the battery through the carbon button and indicator back to the battery.

as in Fig. 3. Make sure that the coin does not touch the metal of the measure. Notice the reading on your indicator. Then press down with the wire on the penny and see whether the needle swings around farther. This demonstrates the basic principle used by Edison in his carbon telephone transmitter. When you speak into the telephone, the pressure of your voice causes the diaphragm of the transmitter to press down on the carbon behind it. This pressure varies the current passing through the carbon. The transmitter diaphragm vibrates to match the sound waves sent out by your voice.

Fig. 3. The needle on the current indicator moves when the penny is pushed down by the wire. This shows how changes in pressure on the carbon vary the current in the circuit.

EXPERIMENT 4. Try other materials in place of the carbon. For example, use powdered chalk. First try it dry, then moisten it with one of a variety of liquids to make it hold together. You might try bicarbonate of soda solution, carbonate of soda (washing soda), salt water. Be careful not to burn your hands with the washing soda. Do not be surprised if you find that the chalk, when wet with some of your solutions, turns out to be a nonconductor. That is what Edison discovered. In place of the carbon or chalk, fill your measure with table salt and repeat the experiment. Try it dry and then moistened. Try clay both dry and wet with the same solutions used with the chalk. Edison did not rest when he found one material suitable for an experiment. He systematically tried one thing after another until he had tried everything that might logically be expected to work.

EXPERIMENT 5. In place of the carbon button, try a variety of fruit pits or seeds from the garden, the woods or the kitchen shelf. Among the most common tried by Edison were pumpkin seeds, peach pits, wild cherry pits, cantaloupe seeds, caraway seeds. Use anything you have at hand that seems of suitable size. Put it in the circuit in place of the carbon button, and see what happens.

SPEAKING TELEGRAPH OR TELESPECAN

Many of Edison's inventions were original devices never before attempted or even thought of. But others were improvements which succeeded in making the invention of someone else practical and widely useful.

In this latter class is the carbon telephone transmitter. It was Alexander Graham Bell who first discovered how to transmit speech over an electric circuit. In Bell's original telephone, the sound vibrations of the voice made a diaphragm vibrate; the vibrations of the diaphragm then induced weak electric impulses in a magnetic coil. The electric impulses were carried to the other end of the telephone line where they produced similar vibrations in another diaphragm and were changed back into sound waves.

Because the electric impulses were so weak, the speech was carried only faintly and was difficult to hear and to understand. Also the telephone was lim-

ited to a short distance—only a few miles even under ideal conditions.

Edison gave credit to his deafness for the improvements he made in the telephone which make possible our modern long-distance telephone system. He said, "I had to improve the transmitter so I could hear it." Edison helped to make Bell's instrument practical commercially.

In his carbon transmitter, Edison did not depend on the voice alone to generate electric impulses strong enough to travel to the receiver at the other end of the telephone line. He used the carbon button to act as an electric valve governing the flow of a current from a storage battery. The current flowed from the battery to the carbon in the transmitter and then through an induction coil back to the battery. The induction coil is a device to "step up" the pressure (voltage) of an electric current. This stronger current then went out on the main line to the receiving end.

When a voice spoke into the transmitter, the diaphragm vibrations caused the flow of current from the battery to vary. These changes in the current were amplified by the induction coil and sent out on the transmission line. In turn they created similar vibrations in the diaphragm of the receiver. These *receiver vibrations produced sound vibrations that reproduced the speaking voice.*

EXPERIMENT 1. Make a model of a telephone transmitter. The first step is to make a mouthpiece to talk into. For this, you can use a small can such as a frozen-juice can or baby-food can. Take off the top and bottom of the can with a rotary can opener so as to leave the edges smooth. Save the tops. Cut a circle of aluminum foil a little larger than the end of the can. Fasten the aluminum-foil circle over one open end of the can. (See Fig. 4.) This will be your diaphragm.

Next make a carbon button. Wrap a sheet of cardboard around the mouthpiece and fasten it together tightly with cellophane tape. The cardboard should extend about a half inch beyond the diaphragm end of the can. Turn the can over so that the extra length of cardboard is up. Fill the space between the diaphragm on the end of the can and the end of the cardboard with activated carbon and pack it in tightly. Attach the end of a wire to the top you cut off the juice can. You can use cellophane or other tape to fasten the wire to the top. Be sure to use the shiny, outer, unvarnished side. (The inside of a juice can has a varnish coating that will not conduct electricity.)

Tape the wired can top securely over the carbon

Fig. 4. Aluminum foil fastened over one end of the juice can becomes the diaphragm for the telespecan. Cardboard is wrapped around the diaphragm end of the can.

with the wire, shiny side next to the carbon; (Fig. 5) fasten the other end of the wire to one terminal of a 6-volt lantern battery. Now you will need a current indicator (for directions for making a current indicator see Carbon Button, page 34). Connect one wire of the current indicator to the side of the can mouthpiece, first scraping both can and wire. Fasten with cellophane tape. Connect the other current indicator wire to the battery. Your current indicator needle will move and then stay steady.

Fig. 5. Wire is attached to the top of the can with tape; the wired top is then fastened firmly over the carbon. Be sure that the wired side touches the carbon.

EXPERIMENT 2. Now you can test your transmitter. Speak, shout, or whistle loudly into the mouthpiece and watch the needle of the current indicator. The pressure of your voice on the diaphragm produces vibrations that press on the carbon. The result should move the needle and make it swing back and forth as you speak.

This experiment illustrates the principle of the carbon transmitter which made possible the long-distance telephone.

Fig. 6. When you speak into the mouthpiece of the telespe-can, the pressure from your voice on the foil diaphragm produces vibrations that press on the carbon causing the needle of the current indicator to move back and forth.

INSULATION

One of the first things you must learn about electricity is that it is extremely dangerous to touch bare wires that are connected to the house current.

Beware of worn extension cords with frayed or broken covering. Don't let the baby or your pet dog chew on the wire or put a curious finger or nose into an electric socket.

But Edison worked with bare wires. In his day, insulated wire was not available.

One time a near disaster occurred because of the lack of insulation on wires. William H. Vanderbilt, a wealthy New Yorker, had seen Edison's new electric lights and decided to have his house lighted with them.

"After a while," said Edison in describing the incident, "we got the engines and boilers and wires all done, and the lights in position, before the house was quite finished, and thought we would have an exhibit

of the light. About eight o'clock in the evening we lit up, and it was very good. Mr. Vanderbilt and his wife and some of his daughters came in, and were there a few minutes when a fire occurred.

"The large picture gallery was lined with silk cloth interwoven with fine metallic thread. In some manner two wires had got crossed with this tinsel, which became red-hot, and the whole mass was soon afire. I knew what was the matter and ordered them to run down and shut off. It had not burst into flame, and died out immediately.

"Mrs. Vanderbilt became hysterical, and wanted to know where it (the fire) came from. We told her we had the plant in the cellar, and when she learned we had a boiler there she said she would not occupy the house. She would not live over a boiler. We had to take the whole installation out. The house afterward went onto the New York Edison System."

We know now, of course, that insulation is very important to the safety of electric wiring. You should be very careful in your experimenting to avoid fires or shock. Do not leave batteries connected when you are through using them. Be careful that the bared ends of "live" wires do not touch paper or other stuff that might catch fire. Do not touch the bare wire yourself. And do not use the house current for your experiments.

Edison soon found that he needed insulation for his electric wires. He had built a small electric railway in the yard of his laboratory at Menlo Park, New Jersey. When it rained, especially when the downpour lasted several days, the wetness kept the railway from working right.

Fig. 7. Various kinds of wires showing different types of insulation. Notice how much thicker the insulation material is on the larger, heavy-duty wires.

Then, too, Edison was interested in improving the underwater cables to carry telegraph messages for long distances. Much of the current going through the cable was lost in the sea because of faulty insulation.

So Edison started to experiment. He used a 100-foot length of cable and put it under water. Then he measured the cable's resistance to the flow of electric current from the wire to the water. He covered the wire with a great variety of materials in the hope of finding insulation that would offer high resistance to the flow of electric current. He knew that if the wire could be well insulated, much less power would be required to send messages through the cable because less power would be wasted.

In his experiments, Edison tested the resistance of each insulating material to see if he could coat the cable to prevent the loss of power.

EXPERIMENT 1. For this experiment, you will need a 6-volt lantern battery and some insulated bell wire.

Add salt to a glass of water until no more salt will dissolve. You now have what is called a saturated solution. Scrape the insulation off both ends of a piece of bell wire. Fasten one bared end of the wire to one terminal of your lantern battery and dip the other end into the salt solution.

Take another length of wire. Bare the ends and wind one end around the base of a 4- to 6-volt flashlight bulb. Then touch the end contact of the bulb (the center of the base) to the second terminal of the battery. While the bulb is touching the terminal, dip the other end of the wire into the salt solution. This completes the circuit from the battery to the salt solution to the light bulb and back to the battery. (See Fig. 8.) As you complete the circuit the bulb will light and a stream of bubbles will rise from one of the wires of the solution. Change the wires so that the wire attached to one battery terminal is now at-

Fig. 8. When the bared part of the wire is dipped in salt solution, a flashlight bulb will light when its end-contact is touched to the terminal of the lantern battery.

tached to the other. Now the bubbles will start to rise from the other wire.

EXPERIMENT 2. Repeat Experiment 1 but this time dip the insulated part of one wire into the solution instead of the bared end (Fig. 9). Now there will be no bubbles and the bulb will not light up.

Fig. 9. The bulb does not light when the insulated part of the wire is dipped into the salt solution.

EXPERIMENT 3. Again repeat Experiment 1, but now wrap the bared end of one wire with paper to provide a poor insulation. At first there will be no bubbles and the bulb will not light. After a short time, however, when the solution has had a chance to soak through the paper, the bubbles will start to rise and you can see the bulb glow.

EXPERIMENT 4. This time when you repeat the experiment insulate the bared end of one wire with a better insulation. You might wrap cellophane tape tightly around it. Now you will have to wait much longer before the bulb lights up and the bubbles form.

Be sure to wipe the wire ends carefully between experiments, as they will become coated and this will serve as an insulation.

Edison, of course, did not use either paper or cellophane tape in his experiments on insulation, but he did try out a great number of materials such as rubber cloth, cloth coated with tar, and cloth coated with paraffin. Some of them are things you may have around the house. You will want to repeat some of Edison's experiments. The following extracts from his notebooks show some of the materials he used:

"Cable No. 1. One thickness of rubber cloth (white) spirals overlapping about 1/3 and tarred with stiff coal tar.

"Cable No. 2. Three layers of rubber cloth and 3 layers of tar.

"Cable No. 3. Two thicknesses of white rubber cloth wound in opposite directions.

"No. 4. Three thicknesses of cloth tarred with boiled coal tar.

"No. 5. Two thicknesses of cloth each served with hot linseed oil.

"No. 6. Cloth wound on cable. Served with paraffin, then rubber cloth (black), cloth again with paraffin.

"No. 7. Bare wire rubbed with dry hard paraffin. Thin rubber cloth (black) covered with black cement, thin rubber cloth, then cement, then rubber cloth, smoothed down with hard paper [emery paper]."

ELECTRIC LIGHT

If you fly over a big city at night you will see thousands of lights looking like strings of bright jewels. Or if you walk down the main street of your town you will see exciting displays of advertising lights. In either case you should think of Thomas Alva Edison. It was Edison who made it possible to light our homes, offices and streets with electricity—to turn the darkness of night into "Great White Ways."

Although Edison was not the first to experiment with electricity to produce light, he was the first to make electric lights practical. He invented the first light bulb that was long-lasting and dependable. And he found a way to generate electricity on a large scale and furnish it to people's homes to light the lights.

Almost as soon as scientists learned how to produce electric currents, they began to try to use them to make light. About 1802, the great Sir Humphry Davy found that when electric currents were passed through thin strips of metal, the metal was heated to a white heat and shone with a bright light.

That was the first step toward the incandescent light. Incandescent means "glowing with heat." Sir Humphry succeeded in making light with his metal strips but it lasted only an instant because the strips burned up in the air, and then the light went out.

The heat (and so the light) produced by electricity is like the heat produced by friction. If you rub your hand hard on a carpet, you can feel the warmth. If you grind a knife blade on a stone to sharpen it, you must use water to cool the blade or it will become quite warm. You may even notice sparks flying from it. Tires will become hot during a long drive.

The flow of current through a metal wire (or Sir Humphry's metal strips) is a movement of electrons from one atom to another through the metal. An electron is a tiny elementary particle carrying a charge of negative electricity.

The heat is caused by the resistance of the wire to the procession of electrons. The amount of resistance depends on the size of the wire and the strength of the current. The finer and longer the wire, the greater is the resistance; and the stronger the current, the greater the heat produced.

As any substance of high melting point is heated,

it will begin to glow first a dull red, then a bright cherry red, then orange, yellow, and finally white. Foundry men estimate the temperature of metal by its color, and astronomers tell how hot heavenly bodies are by comparing their color with that of a standard scale. From the whiteness of the sun's light, it is known that the temperature of the sun's surface is around 10,000 degrees Fahrenheit.

The heating element of your electric range, hot plate, or electric toaster becomes cherry red; the filament in an electric light bulb heats up much hotter and as a result becomes yellow or even white.

The problem faced by Edison was how to make a metal or other substance hot enough to shine with a bright white light, without destroying the metal by burning it up.

Here are some experiments that will give you an understanding of how Edison solved the problem.

EXPERIMENT 1. Using pliers, hold a piece of wire (a straightened paper clip or hairpin will do) in a gas flame. Use a pot holder or gloves to protect your hand because the heat will pass through the pliers to the handles. Watch the wire change color. You will probably not be able to bring it up to white heat unless you use a blowtorch.

To produce much light by incandescence, bright, white heat is needed. But it is necessary to reach a white heat without melting the metal. So you can understand why platinum, with a melting point of about 3,200 degrees Fahrenheit, was chosen for Edison's early lamp experiments. A substance with a low melting point, or one which would burn up, would destroy itself. Tungsten, which has come into wide use for light bulbs since Edison's day, has a much higher melting point than platinum—6,100 degrees Fahrenheit.

EXPERIMENT 2. Get a flat cork or disk of thin wood or a piece of plastic foam or sponge. You can slice such a disk from an ordinary bottle cork or pry the lining from a pop-bottle cap. In the center of your disk, attach a little birthday cake candle. A good way to fasten the candle in place is to let a little of the melted wax drip onto the disk and then push the bottom of the candle against it. Float the little candle in a shallow pan of water (a pie plate will do). If the candle boat is topheavy and upsets, cut off the bottom half of the candle and try again with just the top part.

When the boat is floating, light the candle and turn a drinking glass bottom side up over the burning candle. Push the glass down until the rim is against the bottom of the pan. You will notice that the candle goes to the bottom, too. At first the water will not go into the glass. This is because the glass is filled with air and there is no room for water.

But the burning of the candle uses up the oxygen in the air. As the oxygen is used, the water will rise in the glass and the little candle boat will bob up with the water. When the oxygen is all gone, the flame will go out. (See Fig. 10.)

Fig. 10. When the oxygen is burned out of the air in the glass, the candle flame goes out.

This experiment shows two things: first, the burning of the candle used up the oxygen that was in the air in the glass. But, more important for the understanding of the incandescent electric light, it also shows that when there is no oxygen in the glass the flame goes out. This means that a glowing filament will not burn itself up in a glass bulb in which there is no oxygen.

This fact, basic to the incandescent light, was not known to Edison when he began to work on his lamp. He found it out by a long series of experiments.

First he baked strips of paper until they turned to carbon. Then he passed an electric current from a battery through the carbon strips to find out how much current it would take to make them glow. The strips burned up instantly.

Then he mounted the carbon strips in a glass jar and pumped out the air with a hand vacuum pump. This produced a partial vacuum but a very poor one. The strips glowed for a few minutes but then they burned up.

Edison tried a large number of other materials for his lamp, hoping to find something that would not be destroyed so rapidly.

He used hard-to-melt metals such as boron, ruthenium, chromium and others. None of them worked as he wanted them to. He could not try tungsten, the filament so widely used today, because, at that time, tungsten was available only as a very hard metal that was almost unworkable; it could not be made into filaments.

Of all the metals Edison tried, platinum turned out to be the most promising. So he began an extensive series of experiments with various platinum-iridium alloys, trying to find the right combination.

Today, a vacuum is still used in some incandescent light bulbs to keep the filament from burning up. Most bulbs of 25 watts or less are vacuum bulbs. Bulbs of 40 watts or higher are kept free of oxygen by another method: they are filled with a gas that does not support burning.

EXPERIMENT 3. If you have Christmas-tree lights packed away in your house, get them out and look at them. One box may be marked "Series" and another "Parallel." The strings of bulbs look alike. Plug them in. They still look just alike.

But there is a simple way to see the difference between them. Disconnect the lights and then loosen or take out one bulb from each of the strings. Now plug them in again. In the parallel string of lights, all the bulbs will burn except the bulb you have unscrewed. The series string is all dark. None of the lamps will light up until you have screwed in the loose bulb. When that one is put back in, the whole string lights up again. The same thing happens when the series string is on the tree and one of the bulbs burns out. The lights all go off and stay off until you replace the bad one.

Fig. 11. All the bulbs in the parallel string of lights are burning with the exception of the one that is unscrewed. The series string is all dark.

There was one difficulty with early electric lights, those old-fashioned carbon arc lights that used to light our street corners and are still used in motion-picture projectors; they were suitable only for use in series because otherwise they required too much current.

The electricity went through the early lights too

easily; there was little resistance to its flow. A number of lamps had to be connected one after the other in series so that resistance to the flow of electricity would be built up. This reduced the current flow enough to make the lamps economical.

Edison wanted a lamp with a great deal of resistance that would give a bright light. He wanted to connect the lamps independently of one another (in parallel) and still keep the use of current low. Thus the flow of current through one lighted lamp or several lighted lamps would be small enough to keep the cost down.

Think of water flowing through tubes between two buckets, as in Fig. 12. If you make the water

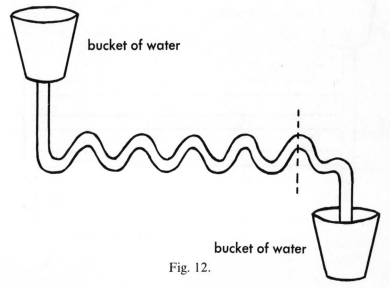

bucket of water

bucket of water

Fig. 12.

flow through many bends as it goes to the other bucket, it will be like adding small resistances or lights in series. It will also take the water quite some time to get from the first to the second bucket. This is like a series current.

In Fig. 13 the water will get to the second bucket more quickly than in Fig. 12 because it goes through three straight tubes at the same time; here the water runs like the current in a parallel circuit.

Notice also that if you shut off one bend in Fig. 12 the flow stops, but if you shut off one tube in Fig. 13, water still flows into the other tubes.

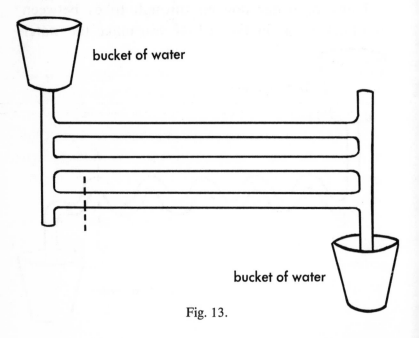

bucket of water

bucket of water

Fig. 13.

Suppose you have two outlets for the water, one a large faucet and the other a fine spray. It would take more water pressure to force water through the tiny holes of the fine spray than would be needed to force just as much water through the large faucet.

It is like that with electric lights. It takes more electrical pressure (known as voltage) to force the current through a lamp with a small filament than would be needed for a large carbon rod.

If you want to get a lot of water in a hurry, you would take your bucket to the large faucet. And if you want a lot of light to illuminate a dark street, you would use big carbon rods in an arc light.

Suppose you have three faucets on the same water pipe. If you turn on one of the faucets you will have a strong flow of water. If you turn on the three faucets at the same time, the amount of water coming from each faucet will not be so great as it was when only one faucet was on. You may have noticed that the water running into the bathtub slows down when somebody starts to run a lot of water in the kitchen sink or the washing machine.

When you have a number of lights connected in parallel, it is like having three faucets on the same water pipe. The electric current (or the water) must be divided among them.

The carbon arc light used big sticks of carbon which did not make much resistance to the flow of current. If the lights were connected in parallel (each getting a separate supply of current), they would burn a tremendous amount of current and would be too expensive. In the days of Edison, no one could supply enough current to light a city.

Edison reasoned that what was needed to make parallel lights economical was a lamp of high resistance. This would require a higher voltage to force the current through the lamp, or less current at the same voltage.

When Edison found a way to produce a high vacuum in his lamps, he also solved the problem of producing lamps that could be used in parallel. Instead of the thick carbon sticks, he used a piece of fine cotton sewing thread which he baked in a kiln until it turned to carbon. The same voltage forced less current through the fine thread than would go through a thick rod. The fine, delicate, brittle thread of carbon was sealed into a bulb from which the air had been pumped out, and thus the first successful, practical incandescent lamp was made.

It glowed. It gave a soft, continuous light easy on the eyes.

Current was turned on in the cotton thread lamp

on October 21, 1879. Then began the famous "death

Fig. 14. Replica of the first successful incandescent bulb.
(*Edison National Monument*)

watch," as it was called in Edison's laboratory. Edison and some of his men took turns watching the lamp day and night for two days. It was still bright after 40 hours. Edison declared that if this lamp could last 40 hours, he could make it last 100 hours. Today the life of a light bulb is standardized at between 750 and 1,000 hours.

FUSE

A very important part of the electric wiring system in your home is the box of fuses. You may not know anything about fuses until suddenly the lights in a part of the house all go out and someone says, "A fuse must have blown."

Actually the fuse box contains guardians of your home. Without fuses there would be danger that your wiring would overheat, the insulation might melt or burn through, and the whole house could catch fire.

It was Edison who invented this important little safety device. He received a patent on it in March, 1880. The patent states that such a fuse should be placed in the circuit of each lamp or other current-carrying device.

The heart of the fuse is a short piece of a metal that will melt at a relatively low temperature. When a circuit that is protected by a fuse is overloaded, for example when too many appliances—toaster, vacuum cleaner, electric iron, etc.—are attached at the *same time, the wire heats up. As soon as the melting point of the metal in the fuse is reached, the metal melts and breaks. Immediately the flow of current*

Fig. 15. Example of an overloaded circuit—too many appliances are attached to one electric circuit.

is cut off. The lights go off. The iron cools. The cleaner is silent.

Nothing happens until you put a new fuse in the proper socket in the fuse box. But in the meantime you have been warned, and you disconnect the vacuum cleaner and the iron, or turn off a few lights or the toaster. It will be wise not to plug them all in

again at once. It is better not to plug in any of them
until someone who understands electricity looks

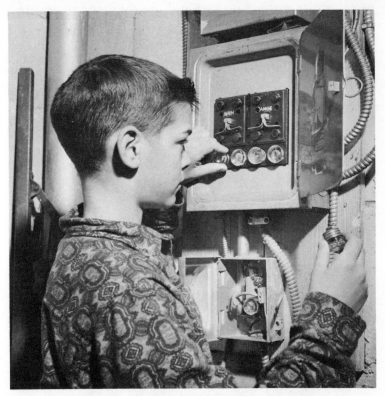

Fig. 16. Boy is replacing a burned-out fuse.

them over to be sure that there is no short circuit or
defective wiring.

Be sure that no one replaces the burned-out fuse
with a penny. The penny will make the current flow
in the circuit, but without the fuse in place, your

house is no longer protected against fire. A wise precaution is to have a supply of extra fuses in the house at all times so that no one will be tempted to use the dangerous makeshift of a penny or a piece of metal foil.

If you examine the fuses in the fuse box in your

Fig. 17. A fuse—the glass window has been removed so that the fuse wire can be seen to better advantage.

home, you will notice that the easily melting wire is enclosed in a glass or porcelain cup with a glass window. Sometimes Pyrex glass is used to provide protection against the heat of the spark or the drop of molten metal that forms as the fuse wire melts.

EXPERIMENT 1. Attach the bared end of a short piece of insulated wire to the center terminal of a 1½-volt flashlight battery (use cellophane tape). Attach another length to the bottom of the battery. Now lay a short length of metal "icicle"—the kind used for Christmas-tree decoration—across the bared free ends of the two insulated wires (Fig. 18). Do not be

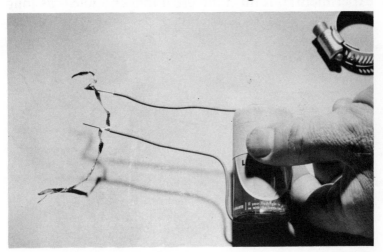

Fig. 18. Metal icicle is laid across the bared ends of two insulated wires connected to a 1½-volt flashlight battery.

surprised if nothing happens. This low voltage probably will not force in enough current to overload your circuit.

Next substitute a 6-volt lantern battery for the flashlight battery (Fig. 19). Now what happens to the icicle? It will probably melt and break. This shows you why the fuse burns out when your circuit is overloaded. The additional voltage in the lantern battery forces more current through the icicle and the resistance of the icicle to all this current produces heat that melts the icicle.

EXPERIMENT 2. Use the lantern battery for this experiment, but this time use a longer icicle—as long

Fig. 19. When the icicle is fastened to a 6-volt lantern battery, the stronger current causes the icicle to melt and break.

a one as you can get. (If you have only broken pieces, tie them together.) Connect one bared end of an insulated wire to each of the terminals of the lantern battery. Touch the ends of the icicle to the free ends of the two insulated wires. What happens?

Fig. 20. A longer icicle does not break because it has greater resistance to the current from the battery.

Probably the icicle will not melt and break. This is because the greater resistance of the longer icicle will prevent much current from flowing in the icicle. There may, however, be enough heat produced by the current to make the icicle feel hot to your fingers. If this happens try a still longer piece of icicle.

These experiments show something about how the fuse protects your home. When all the electricity is turned off in your house—when no lights are burning, no appliances are plugged in, no automatic gadgets are in operation—then there is no current flowing in your wiring. The voltage on your wires remains the same, but because the circuit is now broken, the pressure (voltage) cannot force any current through the wires.

When you flip the switch to turn on a light, however, the circuit is completed and the current starts to flow. The current enters your house through the main cable, and passes through the meter and the fuse box. It goes to the light bulb and heats up the filament so that the metal becomes hot enough to glow and give off light. The current then goes back through the house wiring to complete the circuit.

If you turn on two lights, both of them will light. The voltage on your wires remains the same as it was when only one light was burning, but twice as much current is forced through the wires to complete the circuit. If the voltage remains the same, the amount of heat produced in an electric circuit is in proportion to the amount of current flowing in the circuit. The amount of current is in proportion to the demand made on the circuit by lights or appliances which are being used.

To get a rough idea of how much current will flow
when an appliance is turned on, examine the name-
plate on the appliance and note the wattage rating—
the higher the wattage, the more the current. To cal-
culate roughly the number of amperes (current) that
will flow when the appliance is in use, divide the wattage rating by the voltage rating. Thus a 100-watt
light bulb, designed to operate on 110 volts, would
draw about 0.9 ampere. An electric iron or a toaster
uses more current than a percolator; a percolator
uses more than a light bulb, a 100-watt bulb more
than a 25-watt bulb, and an electric razor more than
a Christmas tree's lights. When you have all these
things attached at the same time, so much current
will flow that the wire will heat up. But before it can
heat enough to endanger your house, the delicate
wire in the fuse will melt and break, cutting off the
flow of current just as though you had flipped off the
switch. With the current flow stopped, the wires immediately start to cool and the danger of fire ends.

ETHERIC FORCE (WIRELESS)

When you watch your favorite programs on television or listen to the radio, you owe thanks to Thomas A. Edison. He made basic discoveries which indicated that it was possible to send electromagnetic waves through space where there were no wire connections. He also took the first steps toward developing the radio tube which picks up and amplifies these wireless signals. (*See Edison Effect, p. 84.*)

In November, 1875, Edison described in his notebooks a "new force" which had been demonstrated in his experiments. Unfortunately, he did not follow up his discovery to put it to work. It was in 1887, twelve years later, that Heinrich R. Hertz, a German physicist, published his description of what appeared to some scientists to be the same phenomenon. This phenomenon which Edison called a "new force" was actually electromagnetic waves. Scientists at that time called the waves Hertzian waves, after Hertz. But the electromagnetic radiation was considered to

*be very similar if not identical to Edison's new force
which he later termed "Etheric Force."*

*Here are some of Edison's experiments in this
field. Although they may look easy to you, do not
be discouraged if your efforts to repeat some of them
are not successful. If you have the courage to try
anyhow, good! You will probably learn a lot by finding out what will not work. That was always Edison's
attitude.*

*Begin with an experiment that is not Edison's but
which will show you some of the things he found out.*

EXPERIMENT 1. Get an ordinary doorbell (not the
expensive chime type). Open it up and you will see
a pair of electromagnets that work a vibrating rod.
The rod serves as a clapper for the bell. Attach bared
ends of two lengths of bell wire to the two screws on
the bell. The other ends of the wires should be attached to the two terminals on a lantern battery or
a general-purpose door-bell battery. (See Fig. 21.) If
the bell rings, you can be sure that both bell and battery are in good working order.

Now bend the clapper over so that the bell will
not ring during your experiments. Connect two lantern batteries (6 volts) so that you will have the use
of 12 volts. To connect them, connect the positive

terminal of one to the negative terminal of the other. Then connect the other two terminals on the batteries to the bell's screw heads. With the batteries connected to the bell the clapper should vibrate,

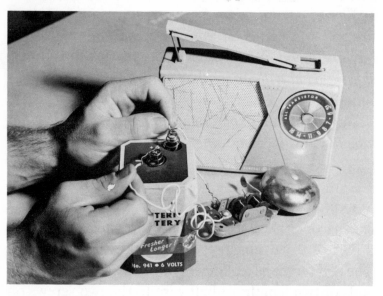

Fig. 21. Bared ends of two lengths of bell wire are fastened to the two screws on the bell. The other ends of the wires are then attached to the terminals of the lantern battery.

making a buzzing sound. Under similar circumstances, Edison drew a spark when he touched the vibrating bar with a wire, or when he attached a wire to the end of the rod and touched the other end of the wire to a large metal object such as a gas pipe or a stove.

If you try this experiment, you will probably not see any spark. This may be because the current you are using does not have as much voltage as that used by Edison. Or it may be because your equipment is not exactly the same as his.

There is another method, however, by which you can show that some waves—those Edison called "etheric force"—are actually produced by the bell-and-battery set up. Carry the assembly to your radio. Turn the radio on but make sure that it is not tuned to any station. Hold the buzzing bell near the antenna wire and listen to the radio. If you hear "static," it is produced by your experimental assembly. This is evidence that your assembly is broadcasting some kind of waves.

Here are some of the experiments Edison tried out in studying "etheric force."

In Edison's first experiment in this field, he connected a battery with an electromagnet as shown in the drawing.

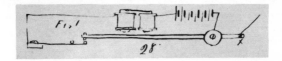

The drawing is taken from one of Edison's notebooks. Edison fastened a steel bar (Stubb's Metal)

at one end and set the other end of the bar vibrating with the magnet. Then he touched any metal part of the magnet or the vibrating bar with an iron or copper wire. A spark jumped across. The larger the piece of wire he touched to the vibrating bar, the brighter was the spark.

Edison attached a wire to the end of the vibrating rod and touched a nail to the end of the wire, drawing a spark. Then he wrote in his notebook: "One of the most curious phenomena is that if you turn the wire around on itself and let the point of the wire touch any other portion of itself you get a spark."

Edison also connected the end of the vibrating rod to the gas pipes in his laboratory and touched a wire to the stove. That drew sparks. He then recorded the result in his notebook: "This is simply wonderful, and a good proof that the cause of the spark is a true unknown force." This statement and the report of the experiment are signed formally by Edison and two assistants, Charles Batchelor and James Adams. It is dated November 22, 1875.

wonderful & a good proof that the cause of the spark is a true unknown force   J a Edson   Nov 22nd 1875   Chas Batchelor   James Adams

This experiment showed very clearly that the "new force" can travel through space without being in a closed metal circuit. Edison placed the battery, magnet, and vibrating rod on an insulated stand. He connected a piece of wire to the end of the vibrating rod and carried the other end of the wire across the room to a stove about 20 feet away. When the wire was rubbed on the stove, it gave out "splendid sparks." When it was permanently connected to the stove, sparks could be drawn from the stove by touching it with a piece of wire held in the hand. When Edison connected the end of the vibrating rod to the gas pipe, sparks could still be drawn from the stove.

Here is the most interesting and dramatic of this

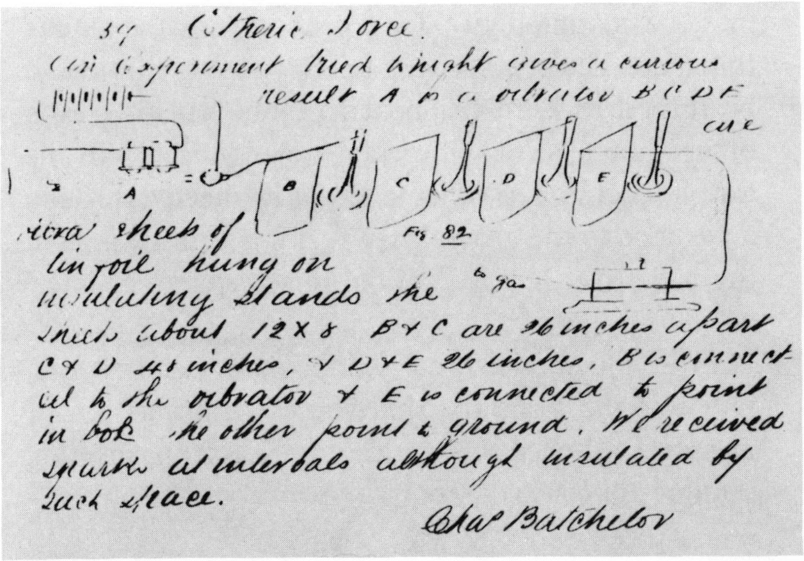

Fig. 82.

series of experiments. Using the same set up as in his first etheric force experiment, Edison put up four insulated stands as shown in the drawing on page 81.

Over the wire attached to each stand he hung a sheet of tin-foil about 8 by 12 inches. The insulated stands were placed some distance apart. B and C were 26 inches apart; C and D were 48 inches apart; and D and E were 26 inches apart. B was connected to the vibrating rod. A spark was obtained from E by attaching a wire and touching the other end of the wire to a large piece of metal.

Edison used this setup for the little black box experiment he sent to the Paris Exposition in 1881. Inside a box with an opening in the cover to look into, he mounted two lead pencils with the points touching. The pencils were held by screws that could be turned to keep the pencil points touching each other. The lead of one pencil was connected to the tinfoil sheet E. The other lead was connected through a gas pipe to the ground. By peeking into the hole in the box cover it was possible to see sparks at intervals.

Edison's etheric force is difficult to demonstrate, but it is the basis for the wireless transmission of messages all over the world and even from orbiting satellites in space.

Fig. 22. Edison looks into the "little black box" at sparks set off by his "etheric effect." (*Edison National Monument*)

EDISON EFFECT (RADIO TUBE)

One of Edison's outstanding discoveries is known as the "Edison Effect." Our modern radio tube and the whole electronics industry are based on this discovery.

After finally developing an electric light that would last for a long time, Edison noticed a light bulb in which the glass had turned dark. Atoms of carbon from the carbon filament had turned to vapor and then condensed on the inside of the glass. But Edison noticed a "shadow" outlined in the black carbon deposit. This shadow, instead of being darker than the rest of the deposit, was actually lighter. It was shaped like one side of the carbon filament in the lamp.

The strange reversed "shadow" made Edison very curious. He wondered what caused it. It seemed to him that the positive side of his filament must be attracting the tiny electrons of the carbon atoms so that the carbon atoms did not reach the glass on the opposite side of the filament with the rest of the deposit.

Edison explored this idea with an experiment. He sealed into a light bulb a flat plate which he attached to a sensitive galvanometer, an instrument for measuring small currents. This, in turn, was connected to the positive side of a battery. When the lamp was turned on, Edison noticed that current also flowed through the wire from this plate even though the plate was not connected to the filament. When the plate was connected to the negative side of the battery, however, no current flowed.

This experiment showed that when the plate was connected to the positive terminal of the battery, the plate, with a positive charge, attracted electrons that were driven off the filament's hot surface. The brighter the light was burning (the hotter the filament), the more current there was flowing from the plate. The driving off of electrons by the heated filament is called "thermionic emission," although engineers speak of it as the "boiling off" of electrons because the process is like the rising of vapor from water when it boils.

EXPERIMENT 1. You can make a simple light bulb, but you probably will not be able to detect the boiling off of electrons from the filament. This is because the current will be at a low level and because your indicator made from the compass (see page 34) is not so sensitive as Edison's galvanometer. For this experiment you will need a battery, preferably a general-purpose 1½-volt doorbell battery, bell wire, magnet wire, a juice glass, and some suitable material to use as a holder—such as polystyrene foam from which some Christmas decorations and flower holders are made, or a small piece of plywood.

Cut a block from the polystyrene foam or the wood so that the juice glass easily slips over it. Cut two pieces of bell wire about 18 inches long. Scrape the insulation off the ends of both pieces of wire. Push the two wires through the foam. The wires should be about one-half inch apart and should come out about one inch on the other side of the foam. Bend the long ends of the wires at the bottom of the foam block, so that the block will sit flat on a plate. The short ends should be on the top of the block. Scrape a two-inch length of magnet wire to remove the varnish insulation. Wrap the ends of the magnet wire around the bared ends of the upright wires, producing a short filament. When, later, you turn the juice glass upside down over the filament, your "light bulb" will be complete.

To keep the filament from oxidizing and burning up, remove the oxygen in the glass. To do this, attach a paper match to the edge of the block. (See Fig. 23.) Bend the match over so that the burning head will not be too close to the juice glass when it is in place.

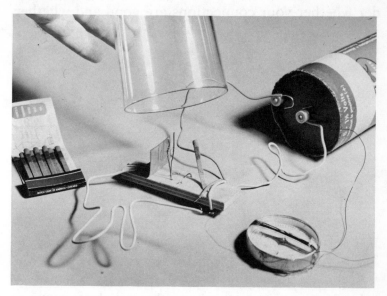

Fig. 23. Before you put the juice glass over the assembly, light the paper match. The burning match consumes the oxygen in the glass.

Light the match with another match, and when it begins to burn evenly, slip the juice glass over the assembly. The burning match will quickly consume the oxygen trapped inside.

Now connect the long ends of the wires to the battery and see whether the filament glows. It should glow a dull red or a little brighter. Darken the room and see whether it gives any light. If it fails to glow, it is probably because your filament has too much resistance and should be made shorter. If you wonder whether your connections are good and whether

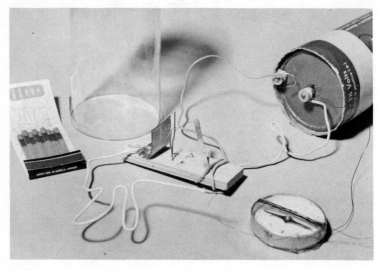

Fig. 24. Compass-current indicator shows whether current is flowing into the "electric light bulb."

current is flowing, check by attaching a compass current indicator to the long ends of the wire leading to the "light bulb" as in Fig. 24. If current is flowing the compass needle should swing over. Never touch the filament with your fingers, because you may get burned even though the filament is not visibly glowing.

Of course you will not expect to see the black deposit on the inside of the glass or the white shadow that Edison observed. Your filament is of copper, not of carbonized thread as was Edison's.

You may be able to insert a plate in your bulb, as shown in Fig. 24, and confirm Edison's experiment on thermionic emission.

EXPERIMENT 2. For this experiment, in addition to the material used in Experiment 1, you will need a strip of metal (you can cut it from a tin can). Drive a nail through one end of the strip to make a small hole. Attach the bared end of a length of bell wire to the hole. (Put the bared end of the wire through the hole and twist it around on itself to make it secure.) Next fasten the metal strip to the block of foam, or plywood. Attach a paper match and light it. Replace the juice glass. Then fasten the wire leading to the metal strip to a current indicator (See page 34.) and attach the indicator to the positive terminal of the battery. If the compass needle swings over, it indicates that electrons are attracted to the positively charged plate from the heated filaments.

Edison discovered the thermionic effect in 1883. Other inventors later modified his bulb and improved it to produce our modern radio tube.

It was in 1904, twenty-one years later, that the British scientist Dr. John A. Fleming put the effect to work. Instead of using a positively charged flat plate to attract the electrons, Dr. Fleming surrounded the glowing filament with a metal cylinder. The cylinder is, however, still called a plate. Because current would flow from filament to plate only when the plate was positively charged, the device acted like a valve to allow the current to flow in only one direction. Dr. Fleming called this tube a "thermionic valve" but engineers in the United States call it a diode tube. When connected to an antenna, the tube could pick up radio waves.

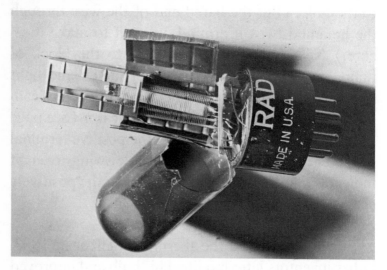

Fig. 25. Cutaway of modern radio tube showing the grid and filament.

An American, Dr. Lee De Forest, added another feature. He put a "grid" between the filament and the plate, located close to the filament. When the filament carried a negative charge, the plate a positive charge, and the grid no charge at all, the tube acted as a rectifier to change alternating current into direct current. (Alternating current, AC, changes its direction of flow rapidly—about 60 times a second—whereas direct current, DC, flows in only one direction.) The tube changed AC to DC by allowing the electron current to flow only from the filament to the plate. When a negative charge was put on the grid, the flow of current to the plate stopped. When a positive charge was put on the grid, the flow to the plate increased.

Fleming and De Forest, working in two different countries, and building on a discovery by Edison, made radio and television possible.

ELECTRIC PEN

One unusual characteristic of Edison's genius was that he was not hindered because the machines he needed to work with had not yet been invented. He just went to work and invented them himself or helped others to perfect them for his use.

Edison had an idea for a machine which would make multiple copies of business papers—the forerunner of the mimeograph, now so common in business offices.

Today no one would think of using a mimeograph if he did not have a typewriter on which to make the stencils. Mimeograph stencils are made by typing without a ribbon on a special kind of paper. The typewriter keys cut the letters in the paper. The stencil is then put on the mimeograph machine where a special ink is forced through the cut letters to print copies. In the early 1870's, when Edison's idea occurred to him, the typewriter was still a very poor instrument and not in general commercial use. Busi-

ness letters and legal documents were written with pen and ink. So Edison made a machine that would cut handwritten letters in a paper stencil. This invention he called the electric pen.

After Edison had the instrument for cutting letters in the stencil, he next had to make an ink that would squeeze through the cut letters to make a large number of copies. He needed an ink that could be pressed through the stencil to make a clear, black impression without smearing or soaking through the paper copy.

Following his usual method of working, Edison got together a large number of materials, put a little of each on paper, and timed the sample to find out which would soak through the paper first. He tried castor oil, olive oil, cod-liver oil, bacon fat, and glycerin. The olive oil, he found, came through first. Castor oil came through fourth. The glycerin did not come through "for some time."

"The most perfect and conspicuous copies ever taken on the autographic press," wrote Edison in his notebook, "were taken this evening with ink formed of printer's ink thinned by castor oil and ground in a mortar some two weeks previously." This entry was dated October 3, 1875.

EXPERIMENT 1. Try making some mimeograph ink as Edison did. Use an old teacup or small bowl

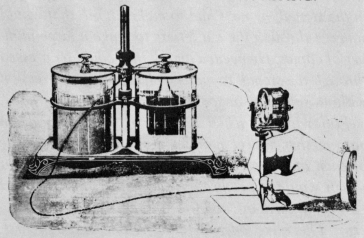

Fig. 26. Early advertisement for the electric pen announced that 5,000 impressions could be made from a single stencil.

as a mortar and an old wooden spoon or utensil handle to grind with. You can probably beg or buy some printer's ink from a printer. Be careful with it; it is very messy. Thin a little of the printer's ink with castor oil and grind it in your teacup mortar. When it is thoroughly mixed, lay it aside to use later on your mimeograph press.

EXPERIMENT 2. Now it is time to prepare the press. Use a smooth board such as a bread board or

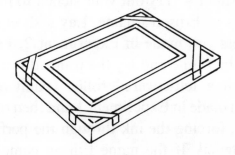

Fig. 27. Drawing of the finished press.

kitchen cutting board. You can buy one in the dime store. Lay a sheet of thin cardboard on the board and fasten it down with cellophane tape. Put four strips of molding together to form a frame. This frame will hold your stencil.

EXPERIMENT 3. Make a stencil first with a hand

tool. To do this, write the name Edison on a sheet of letter paper. Lay the paper on a soft surface such as a rubber or plastic sponge. Holding a large sewing needle upright over the paper and using an up-and-down motion of the needle, guide the needle over the letters so as to trace them with a series of fine perforations. This is your stencil. Edison made a needle which would move up and down rapidly by electricity.

EXPERIMENT 4. Try out your stencil to make multiple copies of Edison's name. Lay a sheet of paper on the press you made in Experiment 2. Fasten the stencil to the frame and lay the frame down over the paper. Roll a felt-covered roller (paint roller) in the ink you made in Experiment 1 and then roll it over the stencil, forcing the ink through the perforations. Lift the stencil. If the name Edison came through clearly, you can change the paper and repeat the process, making as many copies as you want. Edison advertised that his electric pen and duplicating press would make 5,000 copies from a single writing.

EXPERIMENT 5. To follow in Edison's footsteps you will want to have an electric pen with which to cut your stencils. Edison mounted a small, light electric motor on top of a stylus as shown in Fig. 28.

You can make a similar arrangement with your sewing needle. Since small, light motors such as Edison used are not readily available, you can use the "insides" of an ordinary doorbell (not the expensive chime type). You can buy a doorbell like this at the

Fig. 28. Drawing of Edison's electric pen.

hardware store. Take the cover off and you will see a pair of electromagnets. They work a vibrating rod that serves as a clapper for the bell. Bend the clapper back away from the bell so that it is at right angles to the other end of the vibrating rod. This will prevent the noise that would occur if the doorbell were to ring during your experiments. Strap your sewing needle to the clapper with bicycle tape, adhesive tape or masking tape. Connect the two terminals on the doorbell to your lantern battery (the terminals on the doorbell look like two screw heads). When you have the connection made, you should hear a loud buzz.

EXPERIMENT 6. Put a sheet of paper in place over the sponge (see Experiment 3) and hold your doorbell assembly over it so that the needle is upright and in a position to pierce the paper, as in Fig. 29. When the electric pen is connected to the battery the needle

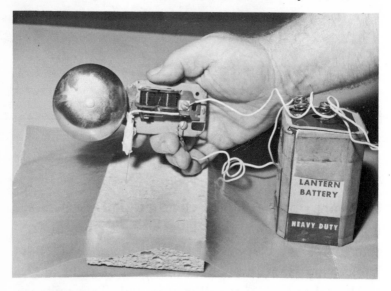

Fig. 29. This is how your "doorbell" electric pen will look when you are ready to make your stencil.

will move rapidly up and down. With this apparatus you can quickly trace letters when you wish to make a stencil.

Now you have an apparatus somewhat like Edison's electric pen, which was the forerunner of the mimeograph.

PHONOGRAPH

Edison's name is most commonly associated with the electric light—probably his greatest achievement. But Edison is also responsible for filling our homes with fine music, for making office work more efficient with the use of dictating machines, and for making law enforcement easier with recording machines and devices for listening in secretly on conversations at a distance.

It was Edison who invented the first phonograph on which these other inventions are based. He received a patent on the phonograph in 1877. The invention caused a great deal of excitement. Many people refused to believe that a machine could record the human voice and later "talk back," repeating exactly what was said into it. People said that there must be a ventriloquist hidden in the room.

If you were to examine one of the first phonographs, you would not notice much resemblance be-

tween that instrument and a modern hi-fi or stereo-phonograph.

The heart of the original instrument was a brass cylinder covered with a sheet of tinfoil. The cylinder was turned by a hand crank and moved along slowly by means of the threads in a steel nut. To record a voice, a person spoke into a kind of trumpet which was funnel-shaped. Inside the funnel was a thin diaphragm which vibrated as the sound waves of the voice struck it. Attached to the vibrating diaphragm was a phonograph needle shaped like a small chisel. The needle made tracings in the tinfoil but because its point was not sharp, it did not tear the foil. The tracings varied in depth to correspond with the varying sound waves of the voice.

To play back the voice, another needle attached to another diaphragm was put in contact with the tinfoil record. As the needle traveled over the tracings it caused the diaphragm to vibrate in the same manner as the recording diaphragm had vibrated when the sound waves of the voice struck it. This reproduced, more or less exactly, the sound of the voice, and whatever had been said was repeated. Not only could the listener understand the words, but he could also recognize who was speaking.

The fault of the device was that the foil "records" had to be played back immediately and then thrown

*away. The tracings were so faint that very little han-
dling would rub them out. Also, it was difficult to*

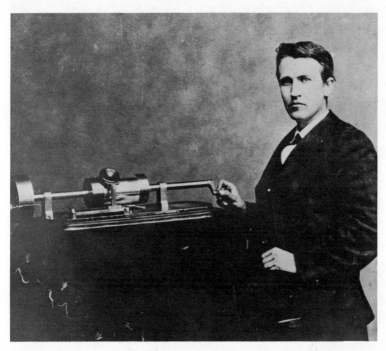

Fig. 30. In April, 1878, Matthew Brady photographed Edison when the inventor demonstrated his "speaking phonograph" before a meeting of the National Academy of Sciences.

*remove the "records" from the machine without tear-
ing them.*

*The playback worked the first time that Edison
tried it. Here is how he describes the experiment and
its exciting climax:*

"Instead of using a disk I designed a little machine using a cylinder provided with grooves around the surface. Over this was to be placed tinfoil, which

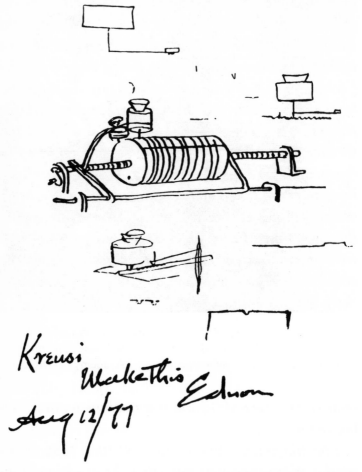

Fig. 31. Edison's sketch for the phonograph with the notation—"Kreusi—Make this . . . Edison."

easily received and recorded the movements of the diaphragm. A sketch was made. The workman who got the sketch was John Kreusi. I didn't have much faith that [the "talking machine"] would work, expecting that I might possibly hear a word or so that would give hope of a future for the idea. Kreusi, when he had nearly finished it, asked what it was for. I told him I was going to record talking, and then have the machine talk back. He thought it absurd. However, it was finished, the foil was put on; I then shouted 'Mary had a little lamb,' etc. I adjusted the reproducer, and the machine reproduced it perfectly. I was never so taken aback in my life. Everybody was astonished. I was always afraid of things that worked the first time. Long experience proved that there were great drawbacks found generally before they could be got commercial; but here was something there was no doubt of."

EXPERIMENT 1. It would be very difficult to make a phonograph like Edison's that would play back your voice. Even Edison himself was surprised when his first invention worked. And you will probably not be able to use the precision methods that Edison used when he designed his instrument.

You can, however, make an instrument that will

demonstrate how the voice can be recorded and re-produced. The more carefully you work, the better will be your results.

For this experiment you will need:

Two small frozen-juice cans and an evaporated-milk can (a little larger than the juice cans)

Heavy-weight, smooth, aluminum foil (not quilted)

A small sheet of glassine

Two finishing nails to use as phonograph needles

Pieces of scrap wood

A 3/8-inch threaded rod and nuts threaded to fit on it

Six washers

Cellophane tape or photographic tape

Airplane cement

A strip of metal (You can cut this from a tin can.)

The first step is to cut a block of wood and mount one of the juice cans. The top and bottom of the can should be removed with a rotary can opener. In cutting the block, follow the shape and dimensions shown in Fig. 32. If it is more convenient to make the block in another size, you can experiment until the different parts of the phonograph fit together. Attach the block to a small piece of wood. Cut two slots in the base of the block so that later you can screw it to the base of the phonograph and adjust it by loosening the screws and pushing (or pulling) the block until it is just the right distance from the cylinder (milk can). Fasten the can in place with a metal strip, screwing the strip down at each end.

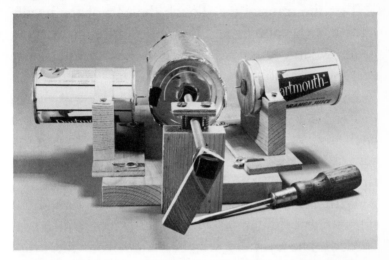

Fig. 32. The blocks that hold the juice cans are cut to fit the shape of the cans. Notice how the blocks are fastened to the base in such a way that the "needles" can be made to touch the metal foil record on the cylinder.

After the can is in place on the block, fasten a piece of glassine over the end that will face the cylinder. Be sure that the glassine is smooth and stretched fairly tight. Fasten it down with cellophane tape. This is your diaphragm. It will vibrate when you speak into the can.

Next, drive one of the finishing nails into a small,

thin piece of wood and fasten the wood with a dab of airplane cement to the center of the diaphragm. Measure carefully so as to mount the needle in the exact center of the diaphragm.

Test the transmitter. Touch the end of the needle lightly with your finger. If everything is in working order, when you speak loudly into the can you should feel the vibration in your finger.

Now attach the block to the wooden base as shown in Fig. 32 by putting a screw with a washer through each slot. With this arrangement, you can loosen the screws and slide the block forward or back and then tighten the screws to hold it in place.

With the transmitter made, you are now ready to set up the cylinder on which your voice will be recorded. The cylinder will be made from the evaporated-milk can. Put a hole in the center of the top and one in the center of the bottom of the can. Work carefully so as to place the holes exactly in the center. They should be just large enough for your threaded rod to pass through. Put the cylinder on the rod and screw a nut on the rod at each end of the can to hold it in place. (See Fig. 33.)

Screw another nut near each end of the rod. These nuts should rest on blocks attached to the ends of the platform. The blocks should be just high enough to hold the rod and cylinder so that the needle on your transmitter can touch the cylinder about midway from the lower side to the upper side. Now nail the blocks to the ends of the platform, and rest the two nuts on the rod on top of these two blocks. Cut two

Fig. 33. The handle that turns the cylinder is fastened to a threaded rod that goes through both ends of the cylinder. The indentations, which can be seen in the metal foil, are a record of the vibrations of the voice.

small strips of wood and lay them on top of the two nuts. Fasten each of these strips in place by screwing them to the blocks with long screws.

The next step is to fasten a handle to the threaded rod so that you can revolve the cylinder. Put a nut on the end of the rod that is to your right when the re-corder mouthpiece is toward you. Put a washer over the nut. Now slip a small piece of wood (of a con-venient size for a handle) with a hole drilled in it on the shaft end. (Figs. 32 and 33 show the handle in place.) Another washer and nut screwed against it on the end will hold it tightly. Wrap a sheet of heavy-weight aluminum foil around the cylinder and fasten it smoothly in place with cellophane or photo-graphic tape.

Now you are ready to try making a record. Be ready to turn the handle as you shout "Mary had a little lamb" or your favorite poem or saying into the transmitter can. You need not turn it fast but you should keep an even speed. The block holding the transmitter should be adjusted so that the needle is touching the cylinder lightly. Now turn the cylinder and shout.

Look closely at the aluminum foil record. You should see a series of tiny indentations which are the record of the vibrations of your voice. Now turn the handle again and shout into the can with a deep growl. Look at the indentations. Examine them closely with a magnifying glass. Then whistle into the can on a high-pitched note. Look at the indenta-tions. See how they differ from those made by the deep growl.

This shows how the foil makes a faithful record

of the changes in your voice. Try singing a tune and then whistling it. Do the tracings look different? Do you want to try to play back your record so that you can hear your own voice?

Fix another can with diaphragm and needle like the one you talked into. This one will be used for listening to your record. Make sure that the needle (finishing nail) is rounded, not sharp. You can smooth it off with a file. Fasten the can to a block of wood as you did the mouthpiece. Use screws and slots so that you can slide the needle up toward the record cylinder and back away from it.

With the needle away from the record, turn the handle to move the cylinder to the left or right until the needle is opposite the beginning of your recording. Then loosen the screws in the slots and move the needle up until it touches the groove lightly. Make this adjustment very carefully so that the needle will not press too hard on the fragile foil but will be close enough to follow the indentations made by your voice.

Turn the handle and listen. You will probably hear something. And your high-pitched whistle will sound different from the deep growl. Don't be disappointed, however, if the sound is not much like your voice and if the words are not distinguishable. Those who listened to the first phonograph were amazed that they could hear anything at all.

QUADRUPLEX

When telegraphy was still young, it became very popular. Soon the traffic was so heavy that the available facilities could not carry it.

Edison had the idea that what was needed was a way to use the same wire to send more than one message at a time. This was what inspired him to invent the duplex (to send two messages at a time) and later the quadruplex (to send four).

In those days it was a great improvement to be able to send four telegraph messages at the same time. Today, the coaxial cable can carry 1,860 telephone calls simultaneously without any sacrifice of privacy or confusion of the messages.

To understand Edison's experiments in this field, it is necessary first to understand the intimate relation between magnetism and electricity. It is possible to produce magnetic action by running an electric current through a wire wound in a coil around a piece of soft iron.

EXPERIMENT 1. Cut off a short length of iron pipe (about one-half inch of one-inch pipe) and then cut the piece in half to make two semicircular pieces. A plumber may be willing to cut the pipe for you. Otherwise, use a hack saw. Wrap bell wire around one of the pieces of pipe to make a coil. Make 40 turns of the wire. The turns may overlap, but be sure to wind them all in the same direction.

Bare the ends of the wire and connect the wire to a 1½-volt ignition battery. When the ends of the wire coil are connected to the battery, you will find that the iron piece will pick up a needle, a paper clip, or other small pieces of iron or steel. (See Fig. 34.)

Fig. 34. Wire coil wrapped around a piece of pipe and connected to a 1½-volt battery forms an electromagnet.

When you disconnect the battery, the magnetism is immediately lost and the metal pieces fall off. Now touch the extra piece of iron pipe to the one you have made into a magnet. Try to pull them apart (Fig. 35). If your battery is fresh, you will probably be

Fig. 35. Touch magnet with the other piece of pipe. Now try to pull the pieces of pipe apart.

surprised at how hard you have to pull. You have made an electromagnet. The most powerful magnets in the world are electromagnets.

EXPERIMENT 2. For this experiment, try to get a bar or rod of soft iron. It does not have to be very large. A horseshoe nail or plain cut flooring nail will

work quite well. Wind 15 turns of bell wire around
the bar or nail. Lay a compass about 4 inches from
the end of the bar so that the needle is pointing north.
Connect the bared ends of the wire coil to the two
terminals of the ignition battery. Watch the compass

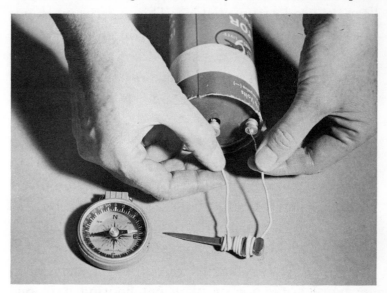

Fig. 36. Compass needle is affected by flow of electric current through the electromagnet.

needle swing over (Fig. 36). Does it swing toward
the east or the west?

Now change the ends of the coil so that the one
that was connected to the positive terminal of the battery is now attached to the negative terminal, and
the one that was connected to the negative terminal

now leads to the positive terminal. This reverses the direction of the flow of current. Now where does the compass needle point? It should swing around to the other side of the compass, although it may be slow in changing. If necessary, tap the compass lightly to keep the needle from sticking. This experiment shows first, that an electric current in a coil around an iron bar will magnetize the bar, and second, that when you reverse the direction of the flow of current in an electromagnet, you reverse the north and south poles of the magnet.

EXPERIMENT 3. Make a telegraph receiver to which you can send messages. You will need a 6-volt battery, a small board about 2 inches wide by 1¾ inches deep, a small strip of aluminum about 2¾ inches × ¼ inch (hardware stores sell it for do-it-yourself projects), magnet wire, four ¾ inch finishing nails, horseshoe or plain cut flooring nail, one finishing nail larger than the horseshoe nail, three small nails, a small bar magnet, and an old frozen-juice can.

Drive the horseshoe nail into the board about ¼ inch from the edge. Wind 200 turns of magnet wire around the horseshoe nail. This will be your electromagnet. Leave 6 or 8 inches of wire at each end of the coil.

Now drive a small finishing nail into the board about 2 inches on each side of the magnet. Scrape the varnish off about 2 or 3 inches of each wire end of the coil, and tie the bright ends tightly around the two small finishing nails so that one end of the coil is attached to each of the nails.

Hammer the big finishing nail into the middle of the board so that its head sticks up a little higher than the head of the horseshoe nail in the coil.

Cut a piece of metal from the juice can in the shape of a dumbbell. The dumbbell should be long enough to reach from the electromagnet to the opposite edge of the board. Nail one end of the dumbbell to the edge of the board. (See Fig. 37.) Bend the dumb-

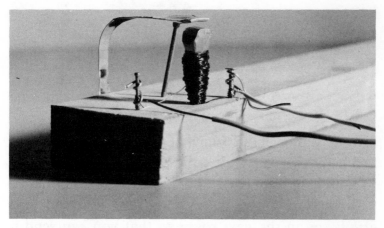

Fig. 37. One end of the metal dumbbell is nailed to the board. The other end touches the large finishing nail when attracted by the electromagnet, but it does not touch the electromagnet.

bell over so that it touches the top of the large finishing nail and not the electromagnet (Fig. 38). Lay a small bar magnet on this end of the dumbbell. It should stay in place by its attraction to the metal. Bend over the strip of aluminum to make an L. Base

Fig. 38. Another view of the dumbbell touching the finishing nail. Notice how the wire ends of the magnet coil are fastened to the small finishing nails.

of L should be about 1 inch. Turn the L upside down and bend over the end of the long (1¾ inches) side to tack it to the board (Fig. 39).

Now you will want to set up a battery and telegraph key in the next room so that you can send a message to your telegraph receiver, which will tap out your dots and dashes.

Connect a long piece of insulated wire to one of the finishing nails next to the electromagnet. Attach the other end to one terminal of the 1½-volt battery. Connect the other finishing nail to one terminal of

Fig. 39. L-shaped aluminum strip as it looks when it is attached to the board. Notice how the long piece of the L is bent so that the L resembles a Z when it is nailed down. Notice, too, how the bar magnet sticks to the dumbbell.

the telegraph key with another piece of insulated wire. Now connect the other terminal of the key to the second terminal of the battery, as in Fig. 40.

Have a friend press the telegraph key to send one long signal, then a short and a long, then one short. Watch and listen to the receiving station. You will see the magnet on the dumbbell go up and down and hear it spell out the initials of Thomas Alva Edison in International Morse Code. Change the wires on the battery to the opposite terminals and watch the receiver as your friend taps the key. Instead of fly-

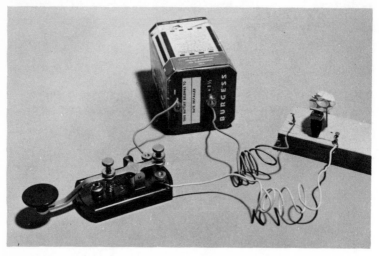

Fig. 40. Here is how your setup will look when the telegraph key is connected to the battery and receiving station.

ing up to tap the aluminum L, the bar magnet will go down toward the electromagnet and tap the nail.

EXPERIMENT 4. Make another receiver that works a little differently. To do this make the electromagnet the same way as in Experiment 3, and tie the ends of the coil to the finishing nail terminals. Drive in the long finishing nail to hold the dumbbell away from the electromagnet. Tack the dumbbell to the board. But this time do not use the bar magnet or the aluminum L. Connect the receiver to the battery and key as before. Now no matter which way you connect the battery, the metal dumbbell will always be attracted toward the electromagnet, and will tap on the nail.

Experiments 3 and 4 have shown how a telegraph works, and that you can operate the receiver from a distance.

EXPERIMENT 5. Use the materials you got together for Experiment 2. Wind a second coil of wire around the iron nail the same number of turns (15), but wind this wire in the opposite direction. Connect the bared ends of the second coil to the terminals of the battery you used for the first coil. Make sure you do not detach the first coil. Now where does the needle point? Although the ends of both coils are connected to the same terminal of the battery, the flow of current in the two coils is in opposite directions because the wire is wound in opposite directions. The magnetic effects caused in the bar oppose each other. But because the current goes through the same number of turns of wire on both coils, the magnetic effects induced in the bar are equal and cancel each other out, hence the compass needle returns to north.

Next, reverse the connections of the second coil to the battery, and notice the compass needle. Now the flow of current in the two coils is in the same direction. The magnetic effect of the current in the second coil is added to that in the first coil. As a result the magnetism in the iron bar is increased and the compass needle will swing over farther than before.

The experiment shows that you can control the magnetism of the iron bar, as shown by the compass needle, in two ways: you can change the direction of the flow of current in either or both coils, or you can change the direction in which one or both coils are wound. A third way of altering the magnetism in the bar is to change the amount of current flowing by connecting another battery so that the voltage is greater in one coil than in the other.

EXPERIMENT 6. Repeat Experiment 5, connecting the ends of the coils to the same terminals of the 1½-volt battery. As in Experiment 5, the current will flow in opposite directions because the coils are wound in opposite directions. In case the two currents do not balance out exactly, add extra turns of wire on one of the coils, or take off turns, until the compass needle points directly north.

EXPERIMENT 7. Use the magnet with two coils wound in opposite directions. Connect a 1½-volt battery to the ends of the second coil; first end to the negative terminal, the other end to the positive terminal. Now in the next room place two more batteries, a 1½-volt battery like the one connected to the second coil, and a 6-volt battery. Connect the negative terminals of both these batteries to one long wire which leads to the first end of the first coil.

Attach another long wire to the second end of the first coil so that the wire may be touched at will to the positive terminals of either of the distant batteries.

Now place the compass near the end of the magnet. Ask a friend to watch the compass needle as you touch first the positive terminal of the 1½-volt battery and then that of the 6-volt battery.

When you touch the 1½-volt battery the compass will point north. The magnetic effects of the two coils balance out. When you disconnect the battery, the compass needle will swing either east or west, depending on which end of the electromagnet you have chosen to use. Now as you connect to the 6-volt battery, the needle will swing the other way. With a key to make and break the circuit, you can use this setup to send messages.

EXPERIMENT 8. Connect a telegraph key to the 6-volt battery. Use the same setup you had at the end of Experiment 7. Connect the negative terminal of the battery to one of the terminals of the key; con-

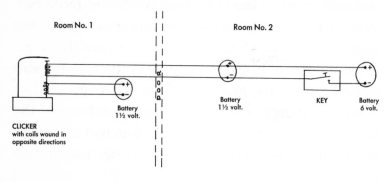

Fig. 41. Drawing of the circuit.

nect the positive terminal of the battery to the other terminal of the key. Now when you press down on the key you complete the circuit, which consists of key, 6-volt battery, coil, and 1½-volt battery. (See Fig. 41.)

Current from the 6-volt battery will flow through one of the coils on the iron bar, magnetizing the bar. If you arrange a dumbbell clicker, such as you made in Experiments 3 and 4, so that when you magnetize the bar the metal clicks, you can send a message from your distant key to the clicker receiving station.

When Edison found these methods of varying the magnetism of the bar—changing the amount of current flowing through the coil, changing the direction of the flow, or changing the direction in which the coil was wound—he combined them so that two messages could be sent at the same time over the same wire.

Edison then arranged to have two messages sent from the distant station to the home station while two others were going out in the opposite direction. The stations could just as well be two cities as two adjoining rooms. For each telegraph line, four operators could be kept busy, two sending and two receiving in each city. This was the quadruplex.

LIST OF MATERIALS YOU WILL NEED

You will have many of these materials in the house. Others you can get from your neighborhood drug store or hardware store. Some of the materials listed here are used in more than one chapter but they are listed under each chapter separately.

CARBON BUTTON
Glass tube
File
Powdered graphite
Insulated bell wire
Nails
6-volt lantern battery
Compass
#30 Varnish-covered magnet wire
Mold
Activated carbon
(Chemical supply store)
Powdered chalk

Materials from kitchen—baking soda, washing soda, salt, fruit pits, seeds, clay (from back yard)

TELESPECAN
Rotary can opener
Frozen-juice cans
Cardboard
Aluminum foil
Bell wire
Activated carbon
Cellophane tape

INSULATION
6-volt lantern battery
Insulated bell wire
Salt
Drinking glass
4- to 6-volt flashlight bulb
Wrapping paper
Cellophane tape
Materials for Edison Insulation—rubber cloth, tar, linseed oil, paraffin, rubber cement, cloth (rags), emery paper

ELECTRIC LIGHT
Pliers
Paper clip or hairpin
Pot holder or gloves
Flat cork or wooden disk
Birthday cake candle
Pie pan or shallow dish
Drinking glass
Christmas-tree lights—series and parallel

FUSE
Insulated wire
1½-volt flashight battery
Cellophane tape
"Icicles" (Christmas-tree decorations)

6-volt lantern battery

ETHERIC FORCE
Doorbell
2 lantern batteries, 6 volts
Bell wire
Radio

EDISON EFFECT
1½-volt doorbell battery
Bell wire
Magnet wire
Juice glass
Polystyrene foam
Paper matches
Compass

THE ELECTRIC PEN
Teacup or bowl
Wooden spoon
Printer's ink (printer)
Castor oil
Bread board or cutting board (dime store)
Cardboard
Molding
Sponge
Sewing needle
Felt-covered roller (paint roller)
Doorbell

Bicycle, adhesive, or masking tape
Lantern battery

PHONOGRAPH
Frozen-juice cans
Evaporated-milk can
Aluminum foil
Glassine
Finishing nails
Pieces of scrap wood
Threaded rod and nuts
6 washers
Cellophane or photographic tape
Metal strip
Magnifying glass

QUADRUPLEX
Iron pipe

1½-volt ignition battery
Bell wire
Horseshoe or plain cut flooring nail
Compass
6-volt battery
Small board
Aluminum
Magnet wire
Finishing nails
Finishing nail, large
3 small nails
Frozen-juice can
Bar magnet
Telegraph key (electronic store. Get inexpensive one sold for code practice.)

INDEX

Set in Linotype Times Roman
Format by Jean Krulis
Manufactured by The Murray Printing Company
and American Book-Stratford Press
Published by HARPER & BROTHERS, *New York*